MORE®
My Ongoing Recovery Experience

Owning It

Workbook 2

This workbook belongs to _____

Hazelden
Publishing

Hazelden Publishing
Center City, Minnesota 55012
hazelden.org/bookstore

ISBN: 978-1-61649-809-2

Editor's note

The names, details, and circumstances may have been changed to protect the privacy of those mentioned in this publication.

This publication is not intended as a substitute for the advice of health care professionals.

Readers should be aware that websites listed in this work may have changed or disappeared between when this work was written and when it is read.

The Twelve Steps are reprinted from *Alcoholics Anonymous,* 4th ed. (New York: Alcoholics Anonymous World Services, 2001), 59–60.

Alcoholics Anonymous, AA, and the Big Book are registered trademarks of Alcoholics Anonymous World Services, Inc.

The content in this workbook is from the Hazelden Betty Ford Foundation's My Ongoing Recovery Experience (MORE®) online aftercare program.

Cover design: Theresa Jaeger Gedig
Interior design: Terri Kinne
Developmental editor: Jodie Carter
Production editor: April Ebb
Copyeditor: Victoria Tirrel

Contents

Overview of the MORE Program

MORE (My Ongoing Recovery Experience) is a program that offers education and guidance on essential recovery topics that will help you successfully manage the critical first year of your recovery. MORE can also be used for those just starting treatment or for those who have been in recovery for a while and want to renew or deepen their knowledge and skills.

Most addiction relapses—taking a drink or using after a period of abstinence—occur within the first eighteen months of recovery, with the majority happening in the first six months after an individual leaves treatment. It is important to identify your high-risk situations that pose a threat to your recovery and to make a plan for them, which will help you avoid relapse. Research suggests that if you can remain abstinent for at least one year after treatment, you have a good chance of staying sober—and maintaining your recovery for the rest of your life.

Overview of This Workbook: *Owning It*

Workbook 2 is called *Owning It* because it will help you make a personal habit of the daily practices and skills that support your recovery.

What Key Topics Are Covered?

This workbook will help you dig deeper into foundational recovery skills, such as relapse prevention, utilizing peer support, improving relationships and communication skills, and learning to put the concepts of Steps One and Two into action in your life. This includes accepting the disease of addiction and moving from self-reliance toward utilizing others' wisdom and experience in recovery for support.

This workbook includes a variety of resources, such as:

- a Thought for the Day meditation or quote to accompany each topic
- education and skill-building on important early recovery topics

- activities that will help you practice self-reflection and put what you are learning into action
- "pocket power" Recovery Resources that you can keep with you for quick reference
- suggestions for Big Book readings on important topics
- websites for other recovery resources

As you complete the lessons in this workbook, you should start to see real growth and transformation in your life as you continue deeper work in recovery principles.

■ ■ ■

Refine Your Daily Schedule

Thought for the Day	*"I will live one day at a time. I will make each day one of preparation for better things ahead. I will not dwell on the past or the future, only on the present."* — *TWENTY-FOUR HOURS A DAY*, JANUARY 1

PLAN EACH HOUR OF YOUR DAY

One of the things that will help you most in early recovery is to stick to a healthy daily schedule where each hour of your time is planned. Having this structure will help you create healthy routines and avoid high-risk situations. Even if you already have a daily schedule, it's important to look at your schedule each week and look for ways to update and improve it so that you eliminate high-risk situations and you have adequate time for spirituality and connection.

ACTIVITY

ASSESS YOUR SCHEDULE

Think about your daily schedule from the past week. Check any of these high-risk situations you encountered.

- ☐ I spent time with a person who was using alcohol or other drugs.
- ☐ I was in a place or situation where other people were using alcohol or other drugs.
- ☐ I experienced high stress.
- ☐ I experienced a lot of conflict with friends, family, or others.
- ☐ I felt extremely happy or festive.
- ☐ I felt very sad or lonely.
- ☐ I was sick or in physical pain.

continued

Duplicating this page is illegal. Do not copy this material without written permission from the publisher.

3

Describe any very high-risk situation you've recently found yourself in.

_____

_____

_____

_____

_____

_____

_____

_____

_____

_____

_____

Update Your Daily Schedule

Take time now to update your existing daily schedule or complete a new Daily Schedule form (found in the Recovery Resources section at the end of this workbook).

Remember to continue to schedule time for the following activities that support your recovery:

- going to Twelve Step meetings
- talking with your sponsor
- connecting with your Higher Power
- doing spiritual activities, such as meditating or taking a walk
- calling friends or family members from your support list
- reading the Big Book or other Twelve Step literature
- caring for yourself: regular mealtimes, regular times for going to bed and waking up, regular exercise, and dealing with physical and/or mental health concerns

■

PLAN TO AVOID RELAPSE

The following tips will help you avoid a relapse by avoiding risky places and risky people.

Tips for Avoiding Risky Places

Check the tips that you are willing to do to protect your recovery.

☐ Take a different route so you avoid certain places.

☐ Ask people to meet you at locations that will not trigger use for you—for example, meet at a coffee shop rather than a bar.

☐ Ask other people to drive, so you aren't tempted to go places you shouldn't.

☐ Turn down invitations to parties or events where alcohol or other drugs might be present.

Tips for Avoiding Risky People

Check the tips that you are most willing to do to protect your recovery.

☐ Politely say no to people you need to avoid.

☐ Honestly tell people that you are in recovery now and need to protect your sobriety.

☐ Get rid of the phone numbers and email addresses of people you used to use with.

☐ Don't go to places where you know risky people will be.

☐ Avoid all contact, even by phone, with risky people.

☐ Use coping strategies if you can't avoid a situation.

If your old schedule exposed you to people, places, stressors, and times of day that posed a high risk for you and your sobriety, make sure you schedule healthy activities in those time slots.

Plan your work, and then work your plan.

ACTIVITY

KNOW YOUR COPING STRATEGIES

Despite your best efforts to plan your daily schedule to avoid high-risk situations, you must be prepared if they do happen. This activity will help you understand three types of potential problems in early recovery, along with the coping strategies you can use to deal with them.

1. **A situation comes up unexpectedly, and you're not prepared.**

   Did you encounter this recently? What happened? Did you use any of the suggested coping strategies? For example, did you call your sponsor or leave the event right away?

   _____

   _____

   _____

   _____

   _____

   _____

   ➡ COPING STRATEGIES:

   • Carry your sponsor's phone number with you at all times.

   • Be prepared at any time to say no. Have a plan in place for unexpected situations.

   • Make sure you have reliable transportation and can leave right away, if needed.

2. **You're in a situation where people just won't take no for an answer.**

   Did you encounter this recently? What happened? Did you use any of the suggested coping strategies? For example, did you say no and walk away, or did you leave the situation right away?

   _____

   _____

   _____

   _____

_____

_____

_____

➡ **COPING STRATEGIES:**

- Remind yourself that your sobriety is more important than people's opinion of you.

- Don't continue to argue—state your no and walk away, or ask that they not ask again.

- Consider the importance of the relationship—do you need to end the relationship?

- Make sure you have reliable transportation and can leave right away, if needed.

3. **You get into a situation and forget what to do.**

Did you encounter this recently? What happened? Did you use any of the suggested coping strategies? For example, did you call your sponsor or a friend right away?

_____

_____

_____

_____

_____

_____

➡ **COPING STRATEGIES:**

- Write out a plan beforehand, and carry it with you.

- Try to avoid this situation in the future, if you can.

- Carry your sponsor's phone number with you; call him or her if you need to while in the situation.

- Take a break from the situation to calm yourself.

■

Duplicating this page is illegal. Do not copy this material without written permission from the publisher.

7

DON'T TEST YOURSELF

If you find yourself in a situation where you are around people, places, or things that remind you of using, give yourself permission to leave immediately. You don't need to stay in a risky situation to test yourself in the presence of alcohol or other drugs. You've taken that test before, and that probably didn't turn out well.

Does your addicted brain ever try to convince you that you can use just once or use just a little? Do you have the temptation to prove that you could be stronger than alcohol or other drugs?

Testing Yourself Statements

Check the box next to the following statements you have said to yourself, or add others:

- ☐ "I'm strong enough to be around alcohol and other drugs now."
- ☐ "I want to see if I can say no to drinking and/or using."
- ☐ "I want to see if I can be around my old friends."
- ☐ _____
- ☐ _____

STINKING THINKING

Although you've made the decision to stop drinking and/or using other drugs, the addicted part of your brain will still try to invent excuses for you to go back to your old routines and old friends—even when those put you at risk for a relapse. It's important for you to recognize this as addicted thinking or "stinking thinking." It's normal to have these thoughts from time to time. The important thing is not to act on those thoughts. Stick to the healthy daily schedule you developed. It will help you protect your serenity and recovery.

It's very easy to forget that being smart, not being strong, is the key to staying sober. Don't put yourself in a risky situation where the odds are stacked against you. Avoiding all temptation to use is your primary goal in early recovery. If you do find yourself in a risky situation, leave immediately and/or call your sponsor or a friend in recovery to make a plan to get out of the situation now—and to avoid it in the future.

■

SUMMARY OF ACTIVITIES

This lesson focused on refining your daily schedule. Remember, "No schedule and no routines = no sobriety." You become smarter and stronger by removing the temptation to use from your day. Remember to counter stinking thinking by flipping the script and turning your thoughts to those that put your recovery first. Make sure you use the blank Daily Schedule form (found in the Recovery Resources section at the end of the workbook) to plan your week. Update and improve this schedule frequently, and keep it with you at all times. If you use a smartphone or computer calendar, make sure you input the schedule into that system so you see it every day.

■ ■ ■

Duplicating this page is illegal. Do not copy this material without written permission from the publisher.

9

LESSON 2

Attend a Meeting

| **Thought for the Day** | *Many meetings, many chances; few meetings, few chances; no meetings, no chances.* |

BENEFITS OF TWELVE STEP GROUPS

It's very important to attend Twelve Step meetings. You may need to try a few groups before you find a "home group" where you feel comfortable attending on a regular basis.

Below are the benefits of attending Twelve Step meetings in groups such as Alcoholics Anonymous (AA) or Narcotics Anonymous (NA):

- You will experience fellowship, strength, and hope.
- You will learn about the Twelve Step principles and ideas.
- You will receive emotional support and feel less lonely and isolated.
- Meetings provide structure and a positive activity to do, instead of drinking or using.
- Meetings will give you a new group of friends who will support your sobriety.
- Meetings will help you with the fear and chaos of early recovery.

"We are going to know a new freedom and a new happiness."

—*Alcoholics Anonymous*

COMMON QUESTIONS AND ANSWERS
ABOUT TWELVE STEP GROUPS

1. **What if I don't agree with people in my group?**

   You may not agree with everything that is said in your group. Take what's helpful and leave the rest. Disagreeing with someone is usually not a good reason to abandon the group. You may not like what people have to say, but it may be what you need to hear. Humility and openness are important traits to cultivate in early recovery.

2. **What if I see a Twelve Step member outside a meeting?**

   Anonymity is an important part of Twelve Step membership. If you see someone outside a meeting, respect this person's privacy. If asked how you know each other, politely say from a social gathering or function. There's no need to give a more detailed explanation.

3. **What if I'm well-known in my community and feel awkward at meetings?**

   It can be difficult to maintain your anonymity when you are well-known. If it will make a difference, you may want to travel to a meeting where people don't know you, or you could try joining meetings online. Nothing replaces face-to-face meetings, however.

ACTIVITY

UNDERSTAND THE BENEFITS OF FELLOWSHIP

The fellowship of AA is a critical part of the strength many members get from attending meetings. This fellowship is important because it is the antidote to isolation and loneliness. Some people in early recovery say they used to feel as though they "didn't belong" or "didn't fit in" with many social groups. In the past, they have tried to hide their drug use, and this caused them to be even more isolated from their non-using friends and family.

1. Can you relate to these feelings? Use the space that follows to describe any ways you were isolated when you were using alcohol or other drugs. Did you stop attending events, such as family holidays, or stop going to church, school, community, sports, or other activities?

   _____

   _____

_____

_____

_____

_____

_____

_____

_____

2. Do you have any concerns that would keep you from attending a Twelve
   Step meeting in the next week? If so, describe them in the space below.

_____

_____

_____

_____

_____

_____

_____

_____

_____

What is the best antidote to alienation and isolation? Friendship. When you
make a connection with another human being, intense feelings of loneliness
decrease. Suddenly if you have a problem, question, or experience you don't understand, you can turn to your fellow AA or NA members for help.

"We cannot really live without the companionship of others. . . .
Do I fully appreciate what the fellowship of A.A. means to me?"

—_Twenty-Four Hours a Day,_ December 9

FAKE IT 'TIL YOU MAKE IT

This is a recovery slogan that can help us get started even when we lack confidence or certainty. The idea is that even if you are not totally comfortable or certain, you will benefit by acting as if you already love meetings. Going to a meeting may be outside of your comfort zone, but if you try it, you will grow, and it's very likely you will grow to really appreciate going to meetings.

SUMMARY OF ACTIVITIES

This lesson focused on helping you understand the benefits of meetings and create the commitment to attend a Twelve Step meeting in the next week. You may need to try a few groups before you find a "home group" where you feel comfortable attending on a regular basis.

■ ■ ■

Cope with Cravings

| **Thought for the Day** | *First things first: If you don't stay sober, not much else will matter. Your first commitment must be sobriety, and the rest will fall into place.* |

UNDERSTANDING CRAVINGS

An urge or craving to use alcohol or other drugs is a normal physical and emotional reaction to stopping drug use. Your body and mind became used to receiving a regular supply of drugs. When you stop taking these, your body and mind still want them.

When you have an urge or craving, you may experience physical symptoms, such as your heart beating faster or your mouth salivating when you are watching a beer commercial. You may encounter cravings or urges without warning, or they may be caused by some trigger, such as seeing your drug of choice or being in a situation where you feel extremely tempted to use, such as being around someone who offers you alcohol or another drug.

When you experience a trigger, such as passing by a place where you used to drink or use, it can cause you to think about using. The more you think about using, the more your body and mind will go into craving mode. In early recovery, these cravings can easily lead to a relapse, or return to drug use.

The graphic below shows how a trigger, such as passing by a bar, can cause us to think maybe we could stop and have just one beer. We start to feel our body and mind crave the beer. This can cause us to act on the thought by using.

Relapse Trigger Process

Trigger ▷ Thought ▷ Craving ▷ Use

ACTIVITY

TRIGGER CHART

It's essential that you know the people, places, things, emotions, and times of day that can trigger your brain to think about using alcohol and other drugs. The chart below shows examples of things that are safe, low risk, high risk, and dangerous for some people in early recovery.

Use the chart on the next page to identify things that are safe, low risk, high risk, and dangerous for your recovery. Write your answers in the space below each heading. Remember that your triggers may be different from the examples provided. Something that is low risk for one person may be high risk for another person.

Trigger Chart

SAFE	LOW RISK	HIGH RISK	DANGER
These are "safe" situations.	These are low-risk situations, but caution is needed.	These situations are high risk. Staying in these is extremely dangerous.	Involvement in these situations is deciding to stay addicted. Avoid totally.

Examples	*Examples*	*Examples*	*Examples*
• feeling grateful • being with friends in recovery • Twelve Step meetings • talking with your sponsor or counselor	• during work • watching TV at home • going out to dinner • driving to and from work or school	• holidays • celebrations where alcohol or other drugs could be present • during or after sex • feeling rejected • having too much free time	• spending too much time alone • feeling resentful • going to concerts or football games where you previously used alcohol or other drugs

Keep managing your people, places, and things.

SAFE	LOW RISK	HIGH RISK	DANGER
These are "safe" situations.	These are low-risk situations, but caution is needed.	These situations are high risk. Staying in these is extremely dangerous.	Involvement in these situations is deciding to stay addicted. Avoid totally.

DEALING WITH CRAVINGS

When you first stop using, cravings can be frequent and intense. With more time in recovery, these cravings will become less frequent and easier to handle. You will experience longer periods of serenity and peace of mind, free from craving. This is because you are practicing abstinence and developing a lifestyle based on personal growth.

To avoid a relapse, careful planning is the key. The next time you have an urge or craving, take the following steps immediately:

1. **Remove yourself from the high-risk situation.**

   Go to a safe place, such as an Alcoholics Anonymous (AA) or Narcotics Anonymous (NA) meeting, right away.

2. **Talk with a friend in recovery.**

   Remember, thoughts about using are not a sign of weakness. Talking about what you're experiencing can help to soften or end the urge. Others know exactly what you're going through.

3. **Remember HALT—hungry, angry, lonely, or tired.**

   Make sure you are not too hungry, angry, lonely, or tired. These feelings can lead to relapse.

SUMMARY OF ACTIVITIES

This lesson taught you about the Relapse Trigger Process (trigger, thought, craving, use) and how to deal with cravings and high-risk situations.

■ ■ ■

LESSON 4

Step One: Understand the Mind

Thought for the Day	*Acceptance means being at peace with something that once deeply troubled you.*

STEP ONE

This lesson will focus on helping you understand what it means to have a mind that can't give up using alcohol or other drugs.

Step One:

"We admitted we were powerless over alcohol [or other drugs]—
that our lives had become unmanageable."

Step One helps identify the problem so you can embrace it.

The truths of the problem are as follows:

1. You have a body that can't handle alcohol or other drugs.

2. You have a mind that can't give them up.

3. In your active addiction, you had no spiritual connection to a Higher Power that could help you.

WHAT DOES IT MEAN TO HAVE A MIND THAT CAN'T GIVE UP ALCOHOL OR OTHER DRUGS?

Even when people who have an addiction know they can't use alcohol or any other drug safely, they may still take that first drink, first snort, or first hit, partly because of their mind. They remember the good feelings they had the last time they used their drug of choice.

The symptoms of this mental obsession are feeling restless, irritable, or discontented. When you have the urge to try just one drink or hit, this is your mind looking for a way to feel better and more content. You may start to think fondly about the last time you used. This made you feel better, but then cravings to use really kicked in. Soon you couldn't stop thinking about drinking or using other drugs as a way to make yourself feel better. But once you started, you couldn't stop. Your mind leads you to start drinking or using, and then your body won't let you stop.

What Does the Big Book Say about This Mental Dilemma?

In the Big Book ("The Doctor's Opinion"), Dr. Silkworth explains that when practicing alcoholics are not drinking, they feel restless, irritable, and discontented until "they can again experience the sense of ease and comfort which comes at once by taking a few drinks—drinks which they see others taking with impunity."

The Big Book also tells us that this cycle is "repeated over and over, and unless this person can experience an entire psychic change there is very little hope of his recovery." And that is the role of the Twelve Steps—to help you make this psychic change.

Once a psychic change has taken place, the very same person who seemed hopeless before has no trouble controlling the urge to drink. The only thing necessary is following a few simple rules—the Twelve Steps.

THE MENTAL OBSESSION OF ADDICTION

If you truly understand that you have a mind that can't give up alcohol or other drugs, you will:

- realize that you are powerless even before you begin using; this means that you realize that if you drive by a place where you previously used or you spend time with friends you used with, you may be powerless to keep yourself from using again

- realize that urges and cravings are a part of the recovery process

- call your sponsor or talk to someone else in recovery, and get yourself to a safe place, preferably an Alcoholics Anonymous (AA) or other Twelve Step meeting, when urges and cravings come

ACTIVITY

IN YOUR MIND

Learn more about the mental obsession of addiction by completing the following activity.

Mike's Story

Mike has been out of treatment for a week. Things were going great the first week, but in the second week he is starting to find himself obsessing about his using days, what it felt like to be high, and how good it felt to use. Try as he might, these mental obsessions with using won't go away. He knows that using, even once, will cause him to lose control. Even so, he finds himself searching for the phone number of his dealer.

1. If the consequences of use are so terrible, why is it so hard for Mike to give it up?

   _____

   _____

   _____

2. Can you identify any mental obsessions you have been having this week?

   _____

   _____

   _____

The solution to our mental obsession with using alcohol or other drugs is in working the Steps. You start by working Step One and accepting that addiction is a disease that leaves you unable to use any amount of alcohol or other drugs without losing control.

Once you accept that you are unable to use alcohol or other drugs without losing control, doesn't it make sense that you must practice complete abstinence from all drugs? If you select no, think about why you selected it.

☐ Yes   ☐ No

Remember: you will become stronger each day by choosing not to use.

■

ACTIVITY

YOUR ADDICTION CYCLE

This activity will help you learn more about how the cycle of addiction has played out in your life. Use the space below to write in your answers to the following questions.

1. You feel restless, irritable, or discontented when:

   _____

   _____

   _____

2. What are the good feelings you remember from alcohol or other drugs that replaced the restlessness, irritability, and discontentment?

   _____

   _____

   _____

   _____

3. What was your favorite drink or drug that you associate with those good feelings?

   _____

   _____

It is very important to your recovery to realize at a deep level the powerlessness you have over the disease of addiction. We know we've got Step One when we accept that addiction is a disease that leaves us unable to use alcohol or other drugs without losing control. We have a disease that requires complete abstinence from all drugs.

Remember, we can still feel powerful by making positive choices. We have the power to choose to avoid situations that could cause us to relapse. We can choose to go to Twelve Step meetings such as AA or Narcotics Anonymous (NA) and spend time with sober peers. We become stronger each day by choosing not to use.

■

SUMMARY OF ACTIVITIES

This lesson taught you the concept of powerlessness from Step One with an emphasis on the mental obsession of addiction. It taught the importance of abstinence because addiction is a disease that leaves people unable to use alcohol or other drugs without losing control.

■ ■ ■

Practice Relapse Prevention Strategies

| **Thought for the Day** | *"It's not what you were, it's what you are today."*
— DAVID MARION |

ACTIVITY

AVOID HIGH-RISK SITUATIONS

To help you prevent relapse in early recovery, we have been asking you to set a daily schedule and stick with it. It may seem unnecessary, but it has proven to be helpful for thousands of others, and it can help you, too.

One of your biggest relapse prevention strategies right now is to avoid high-risk situations. Think about your past week, and answer the questions below:

1. Did you encounter times when you had an unexpected urge or craving?

   ☐ Yes   ☐ No

   If yes, how did you handle it?

   _____

   _____

   _____

   If no, what relapse prevention strategies are helping you reduce your cravings?

   _____

   _____

   _____

continued

Duplicating this page is illegal. Do not copy this material without written permission from the publisher.

25

2. Were you able to avoid a situation that could have been high risk for you?

   ☐ Yes   ☐ No

   If you did find yourself in a high-risk situation, what coping strategies did you use?

   _____

   _____

   _____

   _____

   _____

This is a good time to review the Relapse Prevention Plan you created in workbook 1. If you don't yet have a plan, create one now using the plan located in the Recovery Resources section at the end of this workbook. This Relapse Prevention Plan will help you know what people, places, and things are high risk for you—and it will contain strategies on how to avoid or deal with them. You can then plan your daily schedule so that you avoid these high-risk situations each day.

Think about what's working and what's not working for you as you create your schedule for the next week. You can modify the daily schedule you already started or build a new one (using the Daily Schedule form). Reference the Relapse Prevention Strategies handout for a list of strategies to deal with specific types of events or situations. (These documents are found in the Recovery Resources section at the end of this workbook.)

Remember to continue to build time in your schedule for these activities:

- talking to your sponsor
- connecting with your Higher Power
- doing spiritual activities
- going to Twelve Step meetings or spending time with others in recovery
- reading your Big Book and other Twelve Step literature

The next activity will help you remember why it is so important for you to take the time to schedule your days—hour by hour—to make sure you spend time with healthy activities.

■

ACTIVITY

PLAY THE TAPE THROUGH

This activity will help you remember what can happen if you go back to your old ways.

Spend some time thinking about what would happen if you went ahead and had a drink or used a drug when you were in a high-risk situation. Recall your past experiences when doing this activity, both the good and the bad.

1. Play the tape through by writing what could happen in the space below. Think realistically about what could happen if you were to drink or use again. Where would you end up?

_____

_____

_____

_____

_____

2. Is that a place you want to be?

_____

_____

_____

_____

_____

"The greatest prayer is patience."

—*Buddha*

CREATE HEALTHY HABITS

In recovery, we develop the daily habits of attending meetings and calling our sponsor or a friend. We start and end our day with prayer, a Big Book reading, or a meditation. We do these things whether we feel like it or not. In time, they become second nature to us, as automatic as our addictive behavior was in the past. Once we begin to connect with others at a meeting and connect with our Higher Power, the unexpected happens. We are lifted out of the tyranny of addictive thinking.

KNOW YOUR COPING STRATEGIES

Despite our best efforts to plan our daily schedule to avoid high-risk situations, we must be prepared if they do happen. Review the following coping strategies that you can use to deal with problems you encounter.

1. **A situation comes up unexpectedly, and you're not prepared.**

   Coping strategies:

   - Carry your sponsor's phone number with you at all times.
   - Be prepared at any time to say no. Have a plan in place for unexpected situations.
   - Make sure you have reliable transportation and can leave right away, if needed.

2. **You're in a situation where people just won't take no for an answer.**

   Coping strategies:

   - Remind yourself that your sobriety is more important than people's opinion of you.
   - Don't continue to argue—state your no and walk away, or ask that they not ask again.
   - Consider the importance of the relationship—do you need to end the relationship?
   - Make sure you have reliable transportation and can leave right away, if needed.

3. **You get into a situation and forget what to do.**

   Coping strategies:

   - Write out a plan beforehand, and carry it with you.
   - Try to avoid this situation in the future, if you can.

- Carry your sponsor's phone number with you; call him or her if you need to while in the situation.
- Take a break from the situation to calm yourself.

SUMMARY OF ACTIVITIES

This lesson taught you how to update and improve a daily schedule to avoid high-risk situations. It covered coping strategies for high-risk situations or cravings that may still occur. Make sure you use the Relapse Prevention Strategies handout for quick tips on handling challenging situations and keep your daily schedule updated.

■ ■ ■

Step One: Understand the Spiritual Connection

Thought for the Day	*The Twelve Steps are a simple program for complicated people.*

STEP ONE

Step One identifies the problem of addiction, also known as a substance use disorder, so that we can get to work on recovery.

Step One:
"We admitted we were powerless over alcohol [or other drugs]—
that our lives had become unmanageable."

These are the three truths of the problem:

1. You have a body that can't handle alcohol or other drugs.

2. You have a mind that can't give them up.

3. In your active addiction, you had no spiritual connection to a Higher Power that could help you.

If you truly understand the powerlessness of your situation, you also realize that, up to now, you had no way to make this craziness stop.

As the diagram on the next page shows, you are stuck in a vicious cycle:

- Your mind makes you use.

- Your body can't stop when you use.

- After the binge is over, you feel remorse.

Duplicating this page is illegal. Do not copy this material without written permission from the publisher.

31

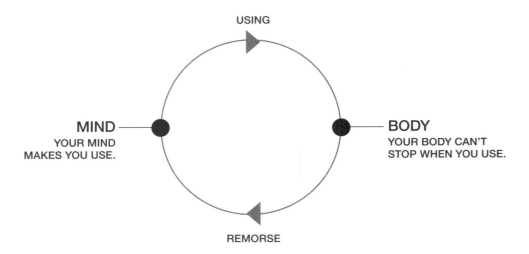

Cycle of Addiction

Feeling sadness, remorse, and self-hatred after using is part of the spiritual aspect of this disease. Internally, we know that this cycle is killing us and hurting others, but we are unable to make it stop. We have no internal will to stop on our own. We lack the internal resources, a Power greater than ourselves, to make it stop. Read the Twelve Steps article (in the Recovery Resources section at the end of this workbook) as a quick reference on all Twelve Steps and how they will help your recovery.

Rachel's Story

Rachel has been in recovery for about three weeks. Everything seems to be going great. She is spending more time with her kids and working the Twelve Step program. Then one day, while driving the kids to soccer, she finds herself driving by her dealer's home.

Without warning, cravings for her drug begin, and the next thing she knows, she is turning into the driveway with the kids still in the car. Searching through her wallet for money, she sees her sponsor's phone number and stops, frozen. A rush of guilt, shame, and self-condemnation comes flooding in. Thoughts whirl through her mind, "How can I be so stupid? What an incredibly terrible parent I am! What a loser—I can't quit!"

Still sitting in her dealer's driveway, Rachel prays for help from her Higher Power. Without this help, she would have been knocking on the door by now. After the prayer, she feels a sense of peace, backs up the car, and drives to soccer practice. Later that night, she calls her sponsor and talks about the situation. They strategize together ways she can get the kids to soccer practice without driving by the dealer's home.

TRYING TO CONTROL YOUR USE DOESN'T WORK

Making rules for yourself about your alcohol or other drug use and then breaking those rules is called loss of control over your use. It's one more sign that you're powerless over alcohol or other drugs. In the Big Book, Dr. Silkworth explains that the addicted person has no effective mental defense against the first drink (or use). The addicted person's defense must come from a Higher Power.

In the past, did you believe you could control your alcohol or other drug use? Explore this by completing the next activity.

ACTIVITY

TRYING TO CONTROL IT

You've probably tried at least a couple of times to control your substance use by cutting down on or switching drugs. You probably thought you could make your life better by setting new rules for yourself. And it may have worked for a short time—but not always. You may have told yourself things like this:

- "I'll use only on the weekends."
- "Hard liquor is bad for me, so I'll only drink beer."
- "I won't drink until after dinner."
- "No more drugs; booze it is."
- "From now on, I'll smoke only pot; no more cocaine for me."
- "I'm going to cut down to five pills a day."

These are just a few examples of how people with the disease of addiction try to set rules for themselves so that they can continue some amount of alcohol or other drug use.

Take a few minutes to list below three ways you tried to set rules for your substance use.

1. _____

_____

_____

2. _____

_____

_____

3. _____

_____

_____

Now, list three times you tried to quit your substance use. Did it work? If so, for how long?

1. _____

_____

_____

2. _____

_____

_____

3. _____

_____

_____

Keep in mind: one symptom of addiction is that you can't stop using when you want to.

■

"Prayer does not change God, but it changes
[the person] who prays."

—*Søren Kierkegaard*

YOU'VE WORKED STEP ONE WHEN . . .

If you can agree that the following are true for you, then you have just worked Step One:

- You have a body that can't handle alcohol or other drugs.

- You have a mind that can't give them up.

- In your active addiction, you had no spiritual connection to a Higher Power that could help you.

To stop the cycle of addiction, you need help from a source greater than yourself. Addiction is a spiritual problem with a spiritual solution. When you embrace this, you'll do the following:

- gain a sense of relief

- have meaning for your struggle

- realize that the solution to this problem isn't all up to you

- realize the problem isn't a lack of character

SUMMARY OF ACTIVITIES

This lesson taught you about the spiritual component of Step One and how the addicted person's defense must come from a Higher Power rather than trying to control use of alcohol or other drugs. Continue to read the Big Book to learn more about how trying to control drug use doesn't work for those with the disease of addiction.

■ ■ ■

Duplicating this page is illegal. Do not copy this material without written permission from the publisher.

35

Strive for HOW
(Honesty, Openness, and Willingness)

Thought for the Day	*"Today, I'm grateful for simple habits that open my heart and mind to recovery."* — IF YOU WANT WHAT WE HAVE

WHY IS <u>HOW</u> IMPORTANT TO YOUR RECOVERY?

HOW (honesty, openness, and willingness) is a common phrase in Twelve Step programs. It represents three key ingredients that are needed to move forward in a successful program of recovery.

Honesty is more than being honest with others. It's about being honest with yourself. While you were drinking and using, your lifestyle was based on dishonesty. It is time to turn that around.

Openness can be very challenging. It is easy to be scared of being rejected if you share the "real you." One way to get over this fear is by reaching out to people in recovery who understand.

Willingness is about commitment and motivation. To maintain sobriety, you need to be willing to put your recovery before everything else. You must commit to do whatever it takes to protect your sobriety at least for today. Your focus is on being willing to stay sober one day at a time.

You can really benefit from being more honest, overcoming your fear of being open, and tapping into your motivation to work your recovery program.

Today I will do one thing.
Change happens one step at a time.

ACTIVITY

PRACTICING HONESTY

While we were using alcohol and other drugs, many of us were far from honest. We often lived in a world of deceit and denial. Recovery demands that we be honest with ourselves, our families, our friends in recovery, and those we have harmed.

Honesty means speaking the truth to yourself and others. At times, however, honesty needs to be tempered with compassion. Never use honesty to purposefully hurt someone. Practicing honesty makes it clear that wisdom is also needed. When you are struggling with an issue of honesty, talk about it with your sponsor or recovery support group.

Learning how to be honest after living dishonestly takes focused effort, and it requires the help of your Higher Power. Making small, daily choices to be honest will help you grow and develop spiritually.

1. Are there small, daily choices you can make to be more honest? Describe them in the space below.

_____

_____

_____

_____

_____

_____

2. How would it change how you feel about yourself if you were being more honest with yourself and with others?

_____

_____

_____

_____

_____

_____

ACTIVITY

PRACTICING OPENNESS

Openness is difficult for most people in recovery. Much of the time, addicts and alcoholics feel that if people really knew who they were and how they felt, they would not like them. Start being open with people you trust, who can understand your work in recovery. A good place to begin might be in your Twelve Step group. Start little by little. Begin by sharing at a meeting and see what happens. Others will respond to your openness.

Can you share your story with someone you trust in the next week? Write his or her name in the space below and write down a brief summary of what you might share with him or her.

_____

_____

_____

_____

_____

_____

_____

_____

_____

_____

_____

_____

_____

Strive for progress, not perfection.

ACTIVITY

PRACTICING WILLINGNESS

Willingness comes from your commitment to do whatever it takes to recover. The Big Book states, "If you have decided you want what we have and are willing to go to any length to get it—then you are ready to take certain steps." Follow the Twelve Steps of Alcoholics Anonymous (AA). You may also need to heed the advice of those who are already sober, even when it does not make sense to you at the time. Willingness is the commitment you bring to your recovery.

How can you practice more willingness in the next week? Could you listen to the advice of your sponsor? Could you go to more meetings? Could you be more accepting of the program of recovery?

_____

_____

_____

_____

_____

_____

_____

_____

_____

_____

_____

_____

_____

_____

_____

_____

HOW

HOW (honesty, openness, and willingness) is the defining principle of Twelve Step groups such as AA and Narcotics Anonymous (NA). It is nearly impossible to drink and use drugs if you live your life in accordance with these simple truths.

Remember that being honest, open, and willing can help you accept responsibility for your actions so you can bring stability back into your life.

SUMMARY OF ACTIVITIES

This lesson taught you about the importance of HOW (honesty, openness, and willingness) in recovery. Remember to practice the strategies you identified in this lesson to help you be more honest, open, and willing in the next week and see how much better you feel after this practice.

■ ■ ■

Duplicating this page is illegal. Do not copy this material without written permission from the publisher.

41

Improve Your Relapse Prevention Strategies

| **Thought for the Day** | *"We cannot rush recovery. You can learn to treat yourself gently, as you would a baby or a kitten, or a sick or injured person lying in a hospital bed. You wouldn't yell at such a person,* Get up! You have work to do! Stop wasting time! *You'd be tender and understanding. You would not begrudge a baby, or someone recovering from illness, time for rest, food, or medicine. Taking some time for meetings is essential to the healing process. Prayer and meditation can help calm you when you feel overwhelmed. . . .*

Today, I treat myself tenderly and patiently."

— IF YOU WANT WHAT WE HAVE |

REVIEW YOUR DAILY SCHEDULE

To help you in early recovery, you have been asked to set a daily schedule and stick with it. It may seem unnecessary, but it has proven to be helpful for thousands of others, and it can help you, too.

Before you take a look at ways to improve your daily schedule, take a moment to think about your accomplishments so far:

1. Have you been working with a sponsor regularly?

   ☐ Yes   ☐ No

2. Have you resisted a craving to drink or use drugs?

   ☐ Yes   ☐ No

3. Are you feeling more motivated to work your recovery program?

   ☐ Yes   ☐ No

continued

Duplicating this page is illegal. Do not copy this material without written permission from the publisher.

43

4. Have you been going to Twelve Step meetings?

☐ Yes ☐ No

If you answered no to any of these questions, what is holding you back?

_____

_____

_____

_____

AVOID HIGH-RISK SITUATIONS

One of your biggest relapse prevention strategies right now is to avoid high-risk situations.

1. Think about your past week. Did you encounter times when you had an unexpected urge or craving? If so, how did you handle the craving?

_____

_____

_____

_____

_____

_____

2. In the past week, were you able to avoid a situation that could have been high risk for you? If you did find yourself in a high-risk situation, what coping strategies did you use?

_____

_____

_____

_____

_____

_____

Remember to keep your Recovery Wallet Card (including your sponsor's phone number) with you at all times. (A blank Recovery Wallet Card is found in the Recovery Resources section at the end of this workbook.) Be prepared to say no to friends who could get you into risky situations. Your sobriety is more important than people's opinion of you.

Think about what's working and what's not working for you as you continue to update your weekly schedule.

■

ACTIVITY

IMPROVE YOUR DAILY SCHEDULE

Use the questions below to improve the daily schedule you already started or build a new one that will help you stay healthy in recovery. (You can find the blank Daily Schedule form in the Recovery Resources section at the end of this workbook.)

☐ Have you experienced any problems with your current schedule? How can you address these problems?

☐ Did you schedule time for Twelve Step meetings?

☐ Did you schedule time to talk with your sponsor and connect with your Higher Power?

☐ Have you scheduled time to complete these early recovery lessons?

☐ Did you schedule regular mealtimes and time for exercise?

☐ Did you schedule time for fellowship? Make time to call a few friends or family members from your Recovery Wallet Card.

☐ Did you schedule time to focus on spiritual things? Why not spend thirty minutes to take a walk in nature and practice serenity sometime this week?

☐ Did you schedule time for medical concerns? If you have health issues requiring doctor's visits and/or medications, schedule the time you need to get these things done.

■

If you aren't sure where you are going,
you may end up somewhere else.

Duplicating this page is illegal. Do not copy this material without written permission from the publisher.

45

MONITOR YOUR THOUGHTS AND ATTITUDES

In addition to planning your time, it is important to also monitor your thinking to see if your thoughts and attitudes could set you up for a relapse. Learn to recognize these attitudes and thoughts by completing the next activity.

ACTIVITY

RELAPSE JUSTIFICATION

Relapse justification is a process that happens in your mind. Although you've made the decision to stop drinking alcohol and/or using other drugs, the addicted part of your brain will still try to invent excuses for you to drink or use. It's important for you to recognize these types of justifications your addicted brain might use so that you can avoid a return to substance use.

Addiction Is Cured

Does your addicted brain ever try to convince you that you can use just once or use just a little?

Check the box next to the following statements you have said to yourself:

☐ "I'm back in control. I'll be able to stop when I want to."

☐ "I've learned I'll only use small amounts and only once in a while."

☐ "This type of alcohol or other drug was not my problem—another one was. So I can use this type and not relapse."

Testing Yourself

Would your brain like to prove you could be stronger than alcohol or other drugs? It's very easy to forget that being smart, not being strong, is the key to staying sober.

Check the box next to the following statements you have said to yourself:

☐ "I'm strong enough to be around alcohol and other drugs now."

☐ "I want to see if I can say no to drinking and/or using."

☐ "I want to see if I can be around my old friends."

Celebrating

Your addicted brain or other people may encourage you to do things that can lead you back to substance use.

Check the box next to the following statements you have said to yourself:

☐ "I'm feeling really good. Using once won't hurt."

☐ "I'm doing so well. Things are going great. I owe myself a reward."

☐ "This is such a special event that I want to celebrate."

What should you do when you find your addicted brain inventing these types of excuses for you to drink or use drugs?

_____

_____

_____

_____

Make sure you use the list of Relapse Prevention Strategies and keep it nearby for quick tips on handling challenging situations. (The Relapse Prevention Strategies are in the Recovery Resources section at the end of this workbook.)

■

SUMMARY OF ACTIVITIES

This lesson taught you how to improve relapse prevention strategies by continuing to identify and avoid high-risk situations, and by improving your daily schedule and list of people you can rely on for support. Make sure you use the Relapse Justification activity to help you monitor your thoughts and attitudes. Reference the Relapse Prevention Strategies handout for quick tips on handling challenging situations. Remember to keep your Recovery Wallet Card (including your sponsor's phone number) with you at all times.

■ ■ ■

Duplicating this page is illegal. Do not copy this material without written permission from the publisher.

47

Work Step One

Thought for the Day | *"The alcoholic at certain times has no effective mental defense against the first drink."*
— ALCOHOLICS ANONYMOUS

THREE TRUTHS

When we were in active addiction, we could not control our use of alcohol and other drugs even though it caused harsh consequences in our lives. This is true powerlessness. For most of us, it's hard to understand why we couldn't stop using despite the problems it caused. Step One helps us identify the problem so we can embrace it and start the work of recovery.

These are the truths of the problem:

- You have a body that can't handle alcohol or other drugs.
- You have a mind that can't give them up.
- In your active addiction, you had no spiritual connection to a Higher Power that could help you.

Cycle of Addiction

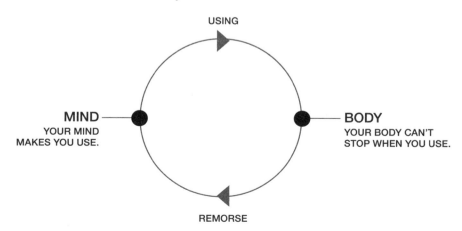

MIND — YOUR MIND MAKES YOU USE.

BODY — YOUR BODY CAN'T STOP WHEN YOU USE.

REMORSE

49

If you truly understand the hopelessness of this situation, you might do the following:

- Quit fighting—let go and let God.
- Start admitting that the problem exists.
- Seek a solution that will solve the problem.

LEARN FROM BILL W.

Bill W., the cofounder of Alcoholics Anonymous (AA), experienced this same vicious cycle with no internal resources to make it stop. If you read through the story of Bill W. carefully, you can see where he accepted each of the Twelve Steps, in order, and how they led to his recovery. If you've been feeling hopeless lately, remember that Bill W. also felt the same way for years.

If you look at the first part of Bill W.'s story, he describes the hopelessness and misery of his situation. He wanted so much to stop drinking and had been trying to do so for years, but it never worked. Finally, he arrived at Step One: admitted his powerlessness over alcohol and realized that his life had become unmanageable. The second half of his journey describes his recovery, his spiritual awakening, his sobriety, and the many years of stability and happiness. The Twelve Steps can work for you, just as they did for Bill W., if you put them into practice each and every day. Bill W. describes his journey in chapter 1 of the Big Book.

ACTIVITY

WHAT DOES STEP ONE MEAN TO YOU?

When we admit powerlessness, we admit that we can't control everything in our lives. We can't control our use of alcohol and other drugs, but we are responsible for our efforts toward recovery.

Think about what Step One means to you. Describe how you feel about Step One in the space below.

_____

_____

_____

_____

We know we've got Step One when we accept that addiction is a disease that leaves us unable to use alcohol or other drugs without losing control.

———

Admitting powerlessness is the first Step. Admitting powerlessness in Step One could end in despair if Step One were all we had, but Steps Two and Three offer a solution to this hopeless problem: believing that a Higher Power can restore us to sanity. You can reference the Twelve Steps article for a list of all Twelve Steps and how they work. (The article is in the Recovery Resources section at the end of this workbook.)

■

SUMMARY OF ACTIVITIES

This lesson taught you how to work Step One, including understanding the benefits of recovery and how addiction impacts your mind, body, and spirit. Read the Twelve Steps article for more information about all of the Steps.

■ ■ ■

Duplicating this page is illegal. Do not copy this material without written permission from the publisher.

51

Make Time for Fun

Thought for the Day	*"Laughter is the sun that drives winter from the human face."* —VICTOR HUGO

THE POWER OF FUN

Recovery is hard work, but part of recovery is achieving balance in your life. So consider balancing your hard work with some lighthearted sober fun.

Laughter helps break tension and stress. It can help you maintain a healthy mental outlook and enjoy the ongoing journey of recovery. Laughter can also help you celebrate recovery and remind you how grateful you are for sobriety.

Having fun reduces stress, whether you're laughing, playing with pets, or flying a kite in the park. All these activities are safe and can be done in safe spaces without triggering the urge to use.

Our old attitudes and limiting attitudes can prevent us from being able to have fun doing healthy activities.

Do some of the following statements ring true for you? Check all that apply.

☐ "I used to need a drink to unwind and have fun."

☐ "Drugs and fun always went hand-in-hand."

☐ "I'm afraid if I let loose a little, I'll want to have a drink."

☐ "Recovery takes all my time and energy. I don't have time for fun."

☐ "It's not possible to have fun while being clean and sober."

ACTIVITY

PLAN SOBER FUN

Look at the list below and check off a few things you would like to try, and then see if you can fit them into your schedule in the next week.

Curious
- ☐ Take a class
- ☐ Go to a museum
- ☐ Try dancing lessons
- ☐ See a play
- ☐ Call a friend
- ☐ Do volunteer work
- ☐ Go sightseeing
- ☐ Visit the zoo
- ☐ Go to a religious service

Creative
- ☐ Redecorate a room
- ☐ Practice photography
- ☐ Try painting or drawing
- ☐ Play a musical instrument
- ☐ Write a poem or song
- ☐ Cook a meal
- ☐ Learn magic tricks
- ☐ Learn to juggle

Adventurous
- ☐ Go hiking or camping
- ☐ Go bird-watching
- ☐ Canoe or kayak
- ☐ Try a new sport
- ☐ Go fishing
- ☐ See an auto show
- ☐ Try climbing
- ☐ Try out a new restaurant

Quiet
- ☐ Explore nature
- ☐ Listen to music
- ☐ Garden
- ☐ Read a book
- ☐ Pray or meditate
- ☐ Write a letter to a friend
- ☐ Spend time with a pet
- ☐ Watch the sunset

Energetic
- ☐ Sing a song
- ☐ Go for a run
- ☐ Visit sober peers
- ☐ Play a sport
- ☐ Hit the gym
- ☐ Clean house
- ☐ Help someone in need

Social
- ☐ Go out to dinner
- ☐ Call a sober peer
- ☐ Join a book club or cooking club
- ☐ See a movie with friends
- ☐ Do a project with a friend
- ☐ Join a sports team
- ☐ Meet a friend for coffee
- ☐ Attend a workshop

Laugh More

Laughter keeps us in touch with ourselves. It brings perspective, helps us heal, and allows us to celebrate our recovery. Celebrate your success in recovery by doing something healthy and fun in the next week. Remember, fun does not need to be expensive. Simple pleasures work, too. Make your friends laugh, go for a hike, take a class, read an inspiring book, see a funny movie, learn something new, hit the gym, play Frisbee, or go swimming. Do something that gets you out of your thoughts for a while and allows you to just "be." Add these activities to your daily schedule.

WHAT CAN YOU GAIN BY ENGAGING IN SOBER FUN?

You may be surprised at the joy of having fun without alcohol or other drugs.

Are you interested in any of these benefits of getting back to healthy habits? Check which ones interest you, and add your own to the end of this list.

☐ Learning a new sport, craft, or skill

☐ Finishing a project you abandoned long ago

☐ Making healthy friends

☐ Laughing without the aid of mood-altering substances

☐ _____

☐ _____

☐ _____

☐ _____

SUMMARY OF ACTIVITIES

This lesson taught you the importance of making time for fun in recovery and offered suggestions for sober fun. Make sure you add some relaxing time for play into your daily schedule. Invite people who are supportive of your recovery to do these enjoyable sober activities with you.

Reflect on Relationships

Thought for the Day	*"One of the worst things about drinking is the loneliness. And one of the best things about A.A. is the fellowship."* —*TWENTY-FOUR HOURS A DAY*, JANUARY 30

ACTIVITY

RELATIONSHIP INVENTORY

Answer the following questions to guide your relationship inventory this week. Are you:

☐ being honest with your sponsor?

☐ being honest with your Twelve Step group?

☐ being supportive, respectful, and honest with your significant other?

☐ being loving (in words and actions) with your children (if you have some)?

☐ acting in ways that care for others' needs as well as your own?

☐ caring for others at the expense of your own needs?

☐ allowing people to take care of their own lives, or are you trying to control them?

☐ humbly seeking support and wisdom from others?

1. Are you holding a resentment toward someone? If so, describe it in the space below.

_____

_____

_____

continued

_____

_____

2. If you let go of this resentment, how would that change how you feel?

_____

_____

_____

_____

3. What are the things that are going well in your relationships?

_____

_____

_____

_____

4. What are some things you can improve in your relationships?

_____

_____

_____

_____

5. Have you been able to focus on being responsible for "cleaning your side of the street" and let others clean up their side?

_____

_____

_____

_____

As part of working your Twelve Step program, it is helpful to take a daily inventory of how things are going in your relationships. Most of all, remember to listen to others, think before you speak, and act instead of react.

■

STICK WITH THE WINNERS

When you reach out to others in recovery, find people who are focused on working a good program. These are the people you want to have coffee or tea with.

It is important to be around people in your Twelve Step group who are actively working their program. There are people in Twelve Step groups who are just hanging around, hoping the program will rub off on them. Find those who are invested in working the program and who will inspire you to invest in it, too. Developing these relationships will help you succeed.

SUMMARY OF ACTIVITIES

This lesson taught you the importance of continuing to perform a relationship inventory to improve important relationships with friends, family, and Twelve Step friends from meetings.

■ ■ ■

Duplicating this page is illegal. Do not copy this material without written permission from the publisher.

59

Check Your Motivation

It is normal for your recovery process to have some ups and downs. Most people run into some bumps in the road. The key is to keep working on your recovery. Your hard work will pay off.

As you spend more time in recovery, you will begin to feel more positive, and your self-esteem will grow. You will have stronger feelings of hope. For a while, your confidence and motivation may still go up and down from day to day. This is natural in early recovery. You can keep your motivation high by going to meetings and by talking with your sponsor and others who are working on recovery.

INTERNAL VERSUS EXTERNAL MOTIVATION

Motivation is that force within you that pushes you forward toward your goals. Internal motivations are driven by your own satisfaction or achievement. Internal motivations include running a three-mile race for general enjoyment and the sense of accomplishment and achievement, or going back to school for the fun and satisfaction of learning.

Internal motivations for recovery include things like wanting to have more respect for yourself and feel better about yourself as a person. They include wanting to feel more responsible and able to give and receive love and respect.

External motivations are often driven by the desire to acquire things or to avoid things that you don't want to have happen. Examples of external motivations in recovery could include quitting drug use to avoid legal consequences or to keep your job.

Duplicating this page is illegal. Do not copy this material without written permission from the publisher.

61

Describe any external motivations you have for quitting drug use.

_____

_____

_____

_____

_____

_____

_____

External motivations, such as keeping your job or avoiding jail time, can work in the short term, but they often don't last long. We are all driven by both external and internal motivations, but it's very important to your recovery to maximize your internal drivers.

When you compare your internal versus external motivation, you want the majority of your motivation to come from the inside. Internal motivation is the best (most lasting) kind of motivation, and it can keep you motivated to work on your recovery.

INCREASE YOUR INTERNAL MOTIVATION

People have different motivations for working toward recovery from the disease of addiction. Some people are motivated to do more for their family. They want to be a better spouse, parent, daughter, or brother. Other people want to resolve health, financial, or work problems. To increase your internal motivation, it's important that you remind yourself of the very personal reasons that you want to remain clean and sober. Wanting to work your recovery program for the benefits it gives your mind, body, and soul is an important internal motivation.

"Nothing can bring you peace but yourself."

—Ralph Waldo Emerson

ACTIVITY

REASONS TO STAY SOBER

Think about the reasons why you want to stay sober. Keep your reasons personal and specific. Make sure your reasons are about gaining something positive for yourself and not about avoiding something negative.

List your reasons below. Provide as much detail as you would like.

Reason 1

_____

_____

_____

_____

_____

Reason 2

_____

_____

_____

_____

_____

Reason 3

_____

_____

_____

_____

_____

continued

Strategies to stay motivated:

- Talk to a friend in recovery about the things that help him or her keep going.
- Go to Twelve Step meetings, such as Alcoholics Anonymous (AA) or Narcotics Anonymous (NA).
- Surround yourself with people in recovery.
- Go out for coffee with people from your Twelve Step group.
- Ask others what motivates their recovery.

■

SUMMARY OF ACTIVITIES

This lesson taught you the importance of staying motivated in recovery. It included information on internal versus external motivation and tips to increase motivation. Make sure you complete the Reasons to Stay Sober activity and keep this list bookmarked so you can look at it often to remind you about the importance of your recovery.

■ ■ ■

LESSON 13

Work Harder at Meetings

Thought for the Day	*Seven days without a meeting makes one weak.*

GO TO MEETINGS EVEN WHEN YOU DON'T FEEL LIKE IT

In early recovery, it's especially important to attend a Twelve Step meeting, such as Alcoholics Anonymous (AA) or Narcotics Anonymous (NA), at least once a week.

For most of us, it's easy to avoid going to a meeting when we feel the following:

- We're too tired.
- We're really busy.
- We're doing well and don't need it.
- It's not worth our time.
- It's too far away.
- We're ashamed with how we are doing in recovery.
- We can't relate to the people there.

Can you relate to any of these feelings that keep you from attending meetings? When you feel like skipping a meeting because you're tired, try to "fake it 'til you make it" and just go anyway. Once you get to the meeting, you may find that you can relate to some of the people in the meeting. Ultimately, you'll see and feel the benefits as you continue to work your recovery program.

Every dream realized started with the decision to try.

Duplicating this page is illegal. Do not copy this material without written permission from the publisher.

65

Tips for Staying Engaged at Meetings

- Arrive early to meetings or stay late. Try to contribute by making coffee, setting up chairs, cleaning up after meetings, and welcoming any newcomers.

- Make sure you talk about your own issues at meetings.

- Call other group members during the week.

- Read recovery literature.

- Talk with your sponsor regularly.

- Try leading a meeting.

ACTIVITY

WORKING YOUR PROGRAM CHECKLIST

This activity will help you tell how well you are working your Twelve Step program. Use the list below as a reminder of what it takes to work a Twelve Step program and connect in recovery.

Which of these actions have you done in the last few weeks to work hard at the Twelve Step program? Check all that apply.

- ☐ Attend meetings on a regular basis (at least once a week is preferred).

- ☐ Talk about your own issues at meetings.

- ☐ Arrive early for meetings and talk to other group members.

- ☐ Make coffee, set up chairs, or clean up after meetings.

- ☐ Welcome newcomers.

- ☐ Socialize with other group members after meetings.

- ☐ Call other group members during the week.

- ☐ Read Twelve Step literature (the Big Book and other literature).

- ☐ Lead meetings when you feel ready.

- ☐ Talk to your sponsor at least once a week.

- ☐ Try to apply the Twelve Steps to your life on a daily basis.

- ☐ Spend time with your Higher Power.

- ☐ Be honest with others.

- ☐ Be open and willing to learn and grow in the program.

Why is it so important for you to "fake it 'til you make it" in a Twelve Step program? Because the program works. Reading the Big Book, working the Twelve Steps, going to meetings—these things will help you stay in recovery, and they work.

■

BASIC IDEAS OF THE TWELVE STEP FELLOWSHIP

The Twelve Step fellowship is founded on the following basic ideas that have helped many people manage their recovery from the disease of addiction:

1. **The Twelve Step foundations work.** The Big Book, the Twelve Steps, the meetings, a sponsor, friends in recovery, a relationship with your Higher Power, and all the other elements of a Twelve Step fellowship have worked to help many people around the world manage their recovery.

2. **Willpower doesn't work.** People addicted to alcohol or other drugs can't stop drinking or using by willpower alone. This is the problem identified in Step One—that you are truly powerless to control how much you drink or use other drugs.

3. **There is no "cure."** Trying to cut back will not help you manage the disease of addiction. The nature of the disease means you have no control over how much you drink or use other drugs. Again, this is about being powerless over addiction.

SUMMARY OF ACTIVITIES

This lesson taught you how to get the most out of meetings as part of working an active Twelve Step program. It included suggestions on how to engage more at meetings and use the Working Your Program Checklist to keep evaluating how well you are working the Twelve Step program.

■ ■ ■

Introduction to Step Two

Thought for the Day	*Faith can move mountains. I pray that I may learn to depend less on myself and more on God.*

UNDERSTANDING STEP TWO

In Step One you admitted you are powerless over alcohol (or other drugs) and that your life has become unmanageable. It takes courage to do the First Step.

Step One defines the problem of addiction:

- You have a body that can't handle alcohol or other drugs.

- You have a mind that can't give them up.

- In your active addiction, you had no spiritual connection to a Higher Power that could help you.

Cycle of Addiction

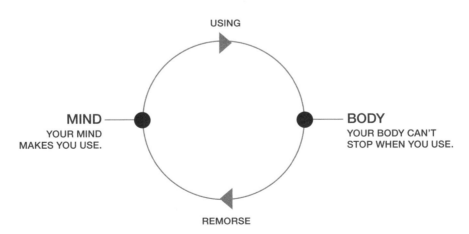

Step Two:

"Came to believe that a Power greater than ourselves
could restore us to sanity."

Step Two is about the solution. In Step Two, you are continuing to define that problem, to see addiction as the by-product of a spiritual problem that requires a spiritual solution. This means you need the help of others; you don't have all the answers. To live an ongoing lifetime of recovery, you will need to find a loving, guiding power you can really trust. This is your Higher Power.

Step Two refers to "a Power greater than ourselves." Does that mean you have to believe in God? Definitely not. A Higher Power can be defined in many ways. Some people call their Higher Power "God." For others, it is the inherent greatness of nature and the universe. For some of us, it may be a group of recovery friends whose collective wisdom is greater than our own. Some call their Higher Power "G.O.D." for "Group of Drunks" or "Good Orderly Direction."

ACTIVITY

DEFINE YOUR HIGHER POWER

Have you started to define your Higher Power yet? If so, describe in the space below.

_____

_____

_____

A belief in God or religion is not necessary in order to work the Twelve Steps. What is necessary is grasping the idea that we can't achieve sobriety alone. If you're like many people in early recovery, you haven't defined your Higher Power yet. That's okay; you don't have to know who or what your Higher Power is right now—you just need to know that you aren't it.

■

To solve the problem of addiction, you need to surrender
to help from outside yourself.

How do you know if you've got Step Two?
You have a sliver of hope because you recognize
the solution to addiction.

WHY CAN'T YOU BE YOUR OWN HIGHER POWER?

During our active addiction, we often put our "faith" in the wrong things (alcohol or other drugs, using friends, our addicted mind) because of our disease. Many of us tried to "play God" during our using days. We believed we had the best plan for ourselves and for others. We alone were given the ability to "be right." We tried to make others bend to our own ideas of how the world should be. Our need for power and control may have crushed any spiritual nature we had.

When we searched for happiness, we found a spiritual emptiness in our lives. We tried to fill that empty place with alcohol or other drugs, money, relationships, material things, or compulsive behavior of one type or another. We found these external answers didn't resolve our internal needs. We had to search for another solution.

Steps Two and Three ask us to seek the spirituality that will give our life meaning.

WHY IS SPIRITUALITY NECESSARY?

Members of Alcoholics Anonymous (AA) often describe the Twelve Steps as a spiritual path. Yet the word "spiritual" immediately points to a dilemma: at times, it is easy to be spiritual, to feel light and joyous, free and forgiving. But what does spirituality mean on Tuesday afternoon at 5:00 p.m. after you've been laid off from your job, your car has a flat tire, and the baby is crying?

How do we merge our spiritual highs with mundane reality and adversity? One answer, says the Twelve Step tradition, is to view spirituality not as a pleasant feeling but as a daily practice. And the basics of this are prayer and meditation.

You may be challenged by urges to drink or use drugs—mental and physical cravings to return to your addiction. Remember that the knowledge that you're addicted to alcohol or other drugs is not enough to keep you sober. If you remain as spiritually bankrupt as you were in your using days, you will return to your old behaviors and, ultimately, substance use.

THE BENEFITS OF STEP TWO

When we work Step Two, we begin to understand the need to surrender and accept help. This surrender helps us feel less loneliness and more peace and serenity. You will find yourself saying the following:

- "I don't need to have all the answers."

- "I am feeling more hopeful. I don't feel so alone."

- "My counselor helped me see things in a new way."

- "I learned a lot from other patients in treatment."

- "It felt good to talk to others about my addiction."

Ben's Story

I felt so much shame about my addiction. If my friends really knew how much I'd been using drugs, I could never face them again. Thankfully, though, my friends didn't know I went to treatment. I could hide my addiction and deal with it by myself.

My sponsor challenged me, however, not to see my addiction as a shameful thing, but as a disease that has a solution.

The solution was to surrender my addiction and shame to my Higher Power. I didn't know how to do that, but I tried by writing a letter of surrender to my Higher Power.

It's been three years since I made that decision—the best decision of my life. Surrendering my addiction to my Higher Power gradually freed me from shame. In fact, I now counsel other men who are hiding their addiction to seek help.

THE THREE PHASES OF WORKING THE STEPS

The Steps can be divided into three phases that show how you grow as you work the Steps.

As you work Step Two (and later, Step Three), you are preparing yourself with a strong foundation for the changes that will happen in Steps Four through Nine and Steps Ten through Twelve.

The Three Phases

Preparation	→	Transformation	→	Continued Transformation

Steps One through Three

The first three Steps prepare you for change. They focus on understanding your disease and knowing and seeking the solution.

Steps Four through Nine

Once you know the problem and the solution, you need to take action. By following these six Steps (also called "Action Steps" in AA), you will begin to see your life transformed.

Steps Ten through Twelve

Recovery is a lifelong journey. These three Steps (also called "Maintenance Steps" in AA) focus on actions you can take to continue your growth and maintain the success you have achieved day by day, for a lifetime.

ACTIVITY

BELIEVE THE SOLUTION

Learn more about the progression of the disease of addiction and the solution that has worked for many others by reading chapter 2 in the Big Book: "There Is a Solution."

This Big Book chapter asks us to believe that there truly is a solution to the problem of addiction, and it involves growing spiritually, working the Steps, and leaning on your friends in recovery for support. Are you willing to believe in this solution of recovery and to use the tools that have worked for many others? Describe how in the space below.

_____

_____

_____

_____

_____

_____

Duplicating this page is illegal. Do not copy this material without written permission from the publisher.

73

SUMMARY OF ACTIVITIES

This lesson taught you the basics of Step Two. It included education about identifying a Higher Power and the spiritual component of recovery.

■ ■ ■

Identify and Own Your Feelings

Thought for the Day	*Neither the past nor the future should control our thoughts or actions today.*

IDENTIFYING EMOTIONS

We feel many emotions every day. Some emotions are more difficult or uncomfortable than others, but all emotions are necessary. When you were using, alcohol and other drugs allowed you to escape from feelings.

Now that you are clean and sober, you may experience strong emotions (such as shame or loss) that you haven't felt for a long time. Or you may still be feeling numb, but your feelings may wake up soon. Let's talk about ways to deal with emotions.

Identifying emotions is an important skill to practice every day. Can you identify how you feel today? Are you feeling sad or frustrated, or confident or delighted? Are you feeling hopeful and happy, or angry and resentful? Being able to label your emotions can help lower your stress level. Try to identify at least three emotions you have every day for the next week. Try to do this without judging the feeling as right or wrong, good or bad. And go beyond labeling your feelings as feeling "fine" or "great" or "bad." If you are struggling with challenging emotions, talk with your sponsor, counselor, or a supportive friend.

The next activity provides a detailed checklist of emotions you can use to identify exactly how you feel each day. After a few weeks of practice, you will be able to more easily explain how you feel without using this list.

Duplicating this page is illegal. Do not copy this material without written permission from the publisher.

75

ACTIVITY

IDENTIFY YOUR FEELINGS

Identifying your emotions is an important skill to practice every day. Look over the list below and check off the words that describe how you are feeling right now. You can have more than one feeling at a time, so check off all the feelings that apply.

☐ amused	☐ glad	☐ pessimistic
☐ angry	☐ grateful	☐ pitiful
☐ annoyed	☐ grief stricken	☐ proud
☐ betrayed	☐ guilty	☐ rageful
☐ caring	☐ happy	☐ regretful
☐ competent	☐ hesitant	☐ resentful
☐ complete	☐ hopeful	☐ revengeful
☐ confident	☐ hostile	☐ sad
☐ delighted	☐ hurt	☐ scared
☐ dependent	☐ immobilized	☐ shameful
☐ despairing	☐ impatient	☐ strong
☐ discounted	☐ inadequate	☐ sympathetic
☐ discouraged	☐ irritated	☐ tender
☐ disgusted	☐ isolated	☐ trusting
☐ distant	☐ jealous	☐ untrusting
☐ eager	☐ joyful	☐ unwanted
☐ encouraged	☐ lonely	☐ useless
☐ envious	☐ loving	☐ vulnerable
☐ excited	☐ mad	☐ wanted
☐ fearful	☐ optimistic	☐ warm
☐ frightened	☐ overwhelmed	☐ wary
☐ fulfilled	☐ patient	☐ weak
☐ giving		

LOOK FOR SIGNS OF GROWTH

As you identify your feelings each day, look for positive signs. How often did you experience serenity or gratitude? The positive choices you are making will lead to these types of feelings. Have you noticed any of these other signs of growth?

- ☐ feeling realistic and hopeful about the future
- ☐ coming to terms with your powerlessness over the disease of addiction
- ☐ beginning to enjoy the small, special moments in life
- ☐ experiencing a range of emotions (highs and lows) as normal reactions to events
- ☐ developing a deeper relationship with a Power greater than yourself

ACTIVITY

THERE ARE NO "BAD" EMOTIONS

Emotions are not bad or good. They just are. It is how we react to them that matters. Talk with your sponsor or a supportive friend about your emotions. For example, pick a difficult emotion that you have been feeling lately (such as anger, shame, failure, hopelessness, guilt, worry, loneliness, or loss) and talk through the following:

1. The difficult emotion is _____ .

2. Describe a time when you had this feeling. What was going on? What happened?

   _____

   _____

   _____

   _____

3. Did you know you were feeling this way at the time? How did you react?

   _____

   _____

   _____

   _____

continued

Duplicating this page is illegal. Do not copy this material without written permission from the publisher.

77

4. What are some positive ways to handle this feeling?

_____

_____

_____

_____

◾

OWNING YOUR EMOTIONS

Owning our emotions means taking responsibility for our reactions to events. This gives us power to change how we feel and how we react.

Do you ever find yourself thinking in "You-Messages" such as the following?

☐ "You make me so mad!"

☐ "Stop making me so frustrated!"

☐ "You make me feel so stupid and sad by talking down to me."

When we use You-Messages, we do not take responsibility for our feelings.
Instead, we can use "I-Messages" like the ones below:

• "I feel angry when . . ."

• "I feel frustrated when . . ."

• "I feel sad when anyone talks down to me."

These types of I-Messages help us own our feelings. You can't always change how people talk to you or the situations that happen. When we say "so-and-so makes me feel this way," we are placing the power for our happiness in the hands of someone else. This is how we begin the "blame game." Avoid this blame game like the plague. It only leaves us feeling helpless, hurt, and resentful. It's important to remember that no one can make us feel anything without our permission. If you own your feelings, then you can do something about them. You have the power to make positive changes.

I-Messages do not judge, blame, threaten, put down, or try to control others. They simply report how you feel, which is rarely challengeable by anyone else. When you make an I-Message, you are taking responsibility for your emotions.

I-Messages inform others about your feelings and may lead to change, but they do not demand change or direct others. They leave the other person free to decide how to react or change to accommodate your needs.

SUMMARY OF ACTIVITIES

This lesson taught you the importance of learning to identify and own your feelings. Make sure you use the activity Identify Your Feelings to identify exactly how you feel each day.

■ ■ ■

Duplicating this page is illegal. Do not copy this material without written permission from the publisher.

79

Recovery Resources

Workbook 2

Daily Schedule

Photocopy this form, so you have one for each day of the week. Then fill in each hour of the schedule.

Daily Schedule

Day of the Week (circle one):   M   T   W   Th   F   Sat   Sun

A.M.   6:00: _____

7:00: _____

8:00: _____

9:00: _____

10:00: _____

11:00: _____

P.M.   Noon: _____

1:00: _____

2:00: _____

3:00: _____

4:00: _____

5:00: _____

6:00: _____

7:00: _____

8:00: _____

9:00: _____

10:00: _____

11:00: _____

Notes:

Reminders

Ask yourself these questions:

- Have I filled in gaps of time?
- Have I scheduled time to connect with my sponsor and Higher Power?
- Have I identified and planned for high-risk situations?
- Did I make my recovery activities a priority?
- Is my day too busy or too stressful?
- Did I schedule time to attend at least one Twelve Step meeting per week?
- Have I shared my plan with others?

Keep this schedule with you at all times.
If you use a smartphone or computer calendar, input the schedule
into that system so you see it every day.

Recovery Wallet Card

Step 1: Write down the names and contact information for three people you know you can count on to support your recovery.

Step 2: Write down three reasons why you want to stay sober. Make sure your reasons are about gaining something positive for yourself and not about avoiding something negative.

Step 3: Write down the names, addresses, and meeting times for nearby Twelve Step meetings you can attend. You can include other recovery resources, such as the addresses and times for addiction treatment meetings or meetings with a mental health counselor or other provider.

Step 4: Keep a copy of the Recovery Wallet Card with you at all times. It's also a good idea to input your supporters into your phone contacts.

Recovery Wallet Card Example

My supporters:	**My reasons for being in recovery:**
Name: Wesley A.	1. Become someone whom I and others respect.
Phone: 612-495-XXXX	2. Heal with my mom/love my mom.
Name: Jennifer A.	3. Be good to myself and others. Happy life.
Phone: 651-375-XXXX	
Name: Mike R. (my sponsor)	
Phone: 651-984-XXXX	*"One day at a time"*

My recovery resources/meetings:	**END YOUR LAPSE**
Name: Sober Friends (Cafe Coffee Shop)	1. ASK FOR HELP TO STOP USING
Address: 9459 W. 28th St., Minneapolis, MN 55408	2. GET OUT OF THE SITUATION
Day/Time: M-F, 7 a.m.	3. REPEAT THE FOLLOWING
Name: Big Book Study Group	• *I made a mistake.*
Address: 4241 Lyndale Ave., Minneapolis, MN 55408	• *I feel guilty, but that's normal.*
Day/Time: Wed., 6 p.m.	• *I will stay calm.*
Name: Solution Seekers (Santi Community Center)	• *One slip does not equal failure.*
Address: 1945 Hawkens St. NW, Eagan, MN 55122	• *I can learn from this experience.*
Day/Time: Sat., 6 p.m.	• *I can recommit to my recovery.*

Your Recovery Wallet Card

Fill out your information.

cut on solid line

My supporters:

Name: _____

Phone: _____

Name: _____

Phone: _____

Name: _____

Phone: _____

My reasons for being in recovery:

1. _____

2. _____

3. _____

"One day at a time"

← fold in half
on dotted line

My recovery resources/meetings:

Name: _____

Address: _____

Day/Time: _____

Name: _____

Address: _____

Day/Time: _____

Name: _____

Address: _____

Day/Time: _____

END YOUR LAPSE

1. ASK FOR HELP TO STOP USING
2. GET OUT OF THE SITUATION
3. REPEAT THE FOLLOWING
   - *I made a mistake.*
   - *I feel guilty, but that's normal.*
   - *I will stay calm.*
   - *One slip does not equal failure.*
   - *I can learn from this experience.*
   - *I can recommit to my recovery.*

← fold in half
on dotted line

Twelve Steps

Where Did the Twelve Steps Come From?

Until 1934, there was no known addiction treatment that worked. Later that year, Bill W. and Dr. Bob started a group called Alcoholics Anonymous (AA) and eventually wrote the Twelve Steps to offer simple, straightforward principles, or basic truths, that people can follow to recover from addiction. The Twelve Steps express the fundamental principles used by members of AA to transform their lives from moral decay and early death to a spiritual fitness needed to keep the disease of addiction at bay.

THE TWELVE STEPS OF ALCOHOLICS ANONYMOUS

1. We admitted we were powerless over alcohol [or other drugs]—that our lives had become unmanageable.

2. Came to believe that a Power greater than ourselves could restore us to sanity.

3. Made a decision to turn our will and our lives over to the care of God *as we understood Him.*

4. Made a searching and fearless moral inventory of ourselves.

5. Admitted to God, to ourselves, and to another human being the exact nature of our wrongs.

6. Were entirely ready to have God remove all these defects of character.

7. Humbly asked Him to remove our shortcomings.

8. Made a list of all persons we had harmed, and became willing to make amends to them all.

9. Made direct amends to such people wherever possible, except when to do so would injure them or others.

10. Continued to take personal inventory and when we were wrong promptly admitted it.

11. Sought through prayer and meditation to improve our conscious contact with God *as we understood Him,* praying only for knowledge of His will for us and the power to carry that out.

12. Having had a spiritual awakening as the result of these steps, we tried to carry this message to alcoholics, and to practice these principles in all our affairs.*

* Reprinted from *Alcoholics Anonymous,* 4th ed. (New York: Alcoholics Anonymous World Services, Inc., 2001), 59–60.

Relapse Prevention Plan

PART 1

This activity will help you create your own personalized relapse prevention plan. This is a three-part activity. Be sure to complete all three parts. Also, periodically update your relapse prevention plan as your routines and environment change.

It is important to identify your high-risk situations or events when you used to drink or use other drugs. These situations or events can be stressful and pose a direct threat to your recovery. It pays to be prepared and plan out the coping strategies you will use.

1. Name four PEOPLE (by first name only to preserve confidentiality) you used with before treatment who are still using and whom you might or will meet again.

    1. _____

    2. _____

    3. _____

    4. _____

2. Write down the names of four PLACES where you used in the past that might still be tempting for you.

    1. _____

    2. _____

    3. _____

    4. _____

3. Name four THINGS that you used to get high (e.g., needles, pipes, money, razors, mirrors, or pills) that might trigger a craving.

    1. _____

    2. _____

    3. _____

    4. _____

4. Describe four HABITS that you had and might still associate with using (e.g., taking a certain route to work, driving by a dealer's house, going to a liquor store, or seeing commercials, logos, or clothing).

   1. _____
   2. _____
   3. _____
   4. _____

5. List four EMOTIONS that could cause a craving (e.g., angry, sad, scared, excited, or bored).

   1. _____
   2. _____
   3. _____
   4. _____

6. List four CONDITIONS that might start a craving (e.g., being out of touch with support people, HALT [hungry, angry, lonely, tired], medical problems, or poverty).

   1. _____
   2. _____
   3. _____
   4. _____

7. Review the high-risk situations/triggers that you listed above. Write down the four most important HIGH-RISK SITUATIONS from these lists.

   1. _____
   2. _____
   3. _____
   4. _____

Relapse Prevention Plan

PART 2

Now that you have made the decision to quit drinking and using drugs, you will begin to feel more confident about staying sober, and this confidence will grow as you continue your recovery journey. However, you still need to plan for risky situations that pose a threat to your recovery. This relapse prevention plan will help you watch for relapse warning signs.

1. List three negative emotional states (e.g., anger, anxiety, depression, frustration, boredom, or grief).

    1. _____
    2. _____
    3. _____

2. What do you intend to do when you find yourself feeling these emotional states?

    1. _____
    2. _____
    3. _____

3. Situations that cause you to experience challenging emotional states and conflict in relationships will put you at a high risk of relapse. List three possible situations and people who might produce challenging emotions or conflict in your life.

    Situations

    1. _____
    2. _____
    3. _____

    People

    1. _____
    2. _____
    3. _____

4. What do you intend to do when you find yourself in these negative emotional states?

   1. _____

   2. _____

   3. _____

5. Describe three examples of social pressure (including verbal or nonverbal persuasion or indirect pressure) that might lead you to return to substance use.

   1. _____

   2. _____

   3. _____

6. What do you intend to do when you find yourself in situations where you feel social pressure?

   1. _____

   2. _____

   3. _____

7. List three positive emotional states that you think could be a problem for you (e.g., happiness, excitement, feeling comfortable, or wanting to celebrate).

   1. _____

   2. _____

   3. _____

8. What do you intend to do when you find yourself feeling these positive emotional states?

   1. _____

   2. _____

   3. _____

9. Give three examples of times when you rationalized your use (e.g., buying a bottle of liquor in case a guest drops in). Denial and a desire for immediate gratification will increase your vulnerability to return to substance use.

   1. _____
   2. _____
   3. _____

10. What do you intend to do when you find yourself rationalizing or denying these situations?

   1. _____
   2. _____
   3. _____

11. A balanced lifestyle has been found to be the strongest defense against relapse. What areas of your life are out of balance?

   1. _____
   2. _____
   3. _____

12. What do you intend to do when you find your life out of balance?

   1. _____
   2. _____
   3. _____

13. What have you been doing (or not doing) for your physical well-being lately?

   _____
   _____
   _____
   _____
   _____

14. What have you been doing (or not doing) for your mental well-being lately?

_____

_____

_____

_____

_____

15. What have you been doing (or not doing) for your spiritual well-being lately?

_____

_____

_____

_____

_____

Keep in Mind: Structure and overall balance are critical for staying in recovery. And remember, if you need support, you can call one of your contacts from your Recovery Wallet Card, including your sponsor, counselor, supportive family members, or friends from meetings.

Relapse Prevention Plan

PART 3

Finding Support: It is important to know where you can find help when you need it.

1. List five people (by first name only) you can call for help when you need it.

   1. _____
   2. _____
   3. _____
   4. _____
   5. _____

2. List five places (addresses and phone numbers) where you can go for help when you need it.

   1. _____
   2. _____
   3. _____
   4. _____
   5. _____

3. List five thoughts that will motivate you to prevent a relapse.

   1. _____
   2. _____
   3. _____
   4. _____
   5. _____

4. If you are unable to follow the strategies in this relapse prevention plan, what can you do?

_____

_____

_____

_____

_____

Remember that your counselor and sponsor are there for you. All you need to do is reach out.

Relapse Prevention Strategies

1. Are there certain times of day that are very stressful for you? Are there days or times (such as payday or the weekend) when you previously used drugs?

    Strategies:

    - Plan to call your sponsor or a friend in recovery at this time.
    - Plan a fun sober activity to do during this time.
    - If possible, attend a Twelve Step meeting during this period of time.
    - Plan to be with other people who are supportive of your recovery during this time.
    - Plan to work on your program during this time—read the Big Book, Twelve Step literature, or a meditation book; spend time in meditation.

2. Are there stretches of time when you will be alone?

    Strategies:

    - Try to limit the long periods of time that you are spending alone.
    - Plan to call your sponsor or a friend in recovery at this time.
    - Plan a fun sober activity to do during this time.
    - If possible, attend a Twelve Step meeting during this time.
    - Plan to be with other people who are supportive of your recovery during this time.

3. Are there events that will be stressful for you?

    Strategies:

    - If possible, avoid this stressful situation.
    - Limit the number of stressful situations you have in your day. Can you say no to something?
    - Before you go to this stressful event, call your sponsor or a friend in recovery. Talk through strategies to handle the stress.
    - Have a plan of "escape" if the situation becomes too stressful—drive separately to the event, for example.
    - Make a plan to call your sponsor or a friend in recovery right after the stressful event.
    - Go to a Twelve Step meeting right after the stressful event.

- Plan an enjoyable sober activity to do right after the stressful event.
- Spend some time in meditation before and after the event.
- Use breathing exercises to calm yourself during the event.

4. Are there any high-risk situations for you this week (people and places you should avoid)? Avoid these high-risk situations—the places where you used to use and places where other people will be using.

Tips for avoiding places:
- Take a different route so you avoid certain places.
- Ask people to meet you at locations that will not trigger use for you— for example, meet at a coffee shop rather than a bar.
- Ask other people to drive, so you aren't tempted to go places you shouldn't.
- Turn down invitations to events where alcohol or other drugs might be present.

Tips for avoiding people:
- Politely say no to people you need to avoid.
- Honestly tell people that you are in recovery now and need to protect your sobriety.
- Get rid of the phone numbers and email addresses of people you used to use with.
- Don't go to places where you know these people will be.
- Avoid all contact, even by phone, with these people.

If you can't avoid a situation, use these coping strategies:
- Ask someone who is supportive of your recovery to go with you.
- Talk through the situation with your sponsor or a friend in recovery before going.
- Write out a plan of how you are going to handle the situation. Create this plan with the help of a friend in recovery. Carry this plan with you.
- Commit to call your sponsor or a friend in recovery right after the event or situation.
- Have an "escape" plan to get out of the situation if it becomes too difficult for you.
- Plan to go to a Twelve Step event right afterward.

About Hazelden Publishing

As part of the Hazelden Betty Ford Foundation, Hazelden Publishing offers both cutting-edge educational resources and inspirational books. Our print and digital works help guide individuals in treatment and recovery, and their loved ones. Professionals who work to prevent and treat addiction also turn to Hazelden Publishing for evidence-based curricula, digital content solutions, and videos for use in schools, treatment programs, correctional programs, and electronic health records systems. We also offer training for implementation of our curricula.

Through published and digital works, Hazelden Publishing extends the reach of healing and hope to individuals, families, and communities affected by addiction and related issues.

For more information about Hazelden publications,
please call **800-328-9000**
or visit us online at **hazelden.org/bookstore**.